MW00605129

# Woman Under Construction

# Tool Book

## Linda G. Hodge

ISBN 978-0-9818790-9-3

Library of Congress Control Number: 2011929603

Edited by Penny Scott

Front and Back Cover Design
Wendy Aguirre – Studio Wende El

Front Cover Photography – Juan Roberts – Creative Lunacy
Creative Art Director – Antoinette Bell

Interior Design – John Sibley – Rock Solid Productions

For information regarding permission or additional copies, contact the publisher:

Printed in the United States

**KNOWLEDGE POWER BOOKS**
A Division of Knowledge Power Communications, Inc.
25379 Wayne Mills Place, Suite 131, Valencia, CA 91355
661-513-0308  Fax:  661-513-0381
www.knowledgepowerbooks.com

# INTRODUCTION

## Dear Overcomer:

In this workbook, you will be provided with key points of each chapter. You will have a time of reflection: brief exercises, along with a Weekly Memory Verse, Weekly Prayer, Weekly Action List for implementation, and conclude with our Weekly Character Building Block Word for you, the "Woman Under Construction." This Tool Book will be our roadmap as we work together throughout this journey of renovation.

Consequently, before we begin our work together, let me assure you that I have the utmost confidence in you. This journey of life renovation will be both rewarding and fulfilling, and you will be pleasantly surprised at your glorious outcome. It is so important that you believe and see the best in you! Consider me as your *"Woman Under Construction"* coach. I will be leading you step-by-step throughout each chapter and will be praying that you receive everything you need from each section.

Each chapter has been thoroughly examined and written with you in mind. However, I must warn you that I'm expecting you to work. That's why it is called a "tool book," that we've coined from the workbook concept. Thus, I will need your participation and involvement in your renovation process. Weekly, you will read a chapter of the book, ***Woman Under Construction,*** and exert yourself in the chapter's activities. I need for you to set aside time daily to work throughout the chapters. This is "your time!" Assign private moments to work toward your personal development. Labor at your own steady pace, and sometimes, you may need to re-read a chapter to fully grasp the total concept of that particular chapter. That's OK. I need you to absorb every written word, concept, analogy and truth told on those pages. So be patient with you, and don't rush through the exercises.

You have been born to WIN! Not to lose! If you are reading this book, then I know you are serious about your spiritual, emotional, and personal development. Half of the work is already done and with your participation in each outlined exercise, I will see you "Over the top."

Put away all doubt, unbelief, and fear. You will cease to be a history student, and begin the fabulous and breathtaking adventure of being a history maker!

Well, with enough said, are you ready to pursue and overtake every giant that has been trying to sabotage your personal growth? If you're ready, it's time to lose yourself from the shackles of defeat. Get in position, get mark, set and let's GO…….

Sincerely,

*Pastor Linda Hodge*

Pastor Linda G. Hodge
Author of *Woman Under Construction*

# TABLE OF CONTENTS

Letter from the Author

# CHAPTER 1

# Construction Site

I trust you have read the First Chapter of the book, ***Woman Under Construction***. That will be our guide and roadmap as we work together throughout this journey of renovation. In constructing a life that will glorify God, and yield a bountiful harvest, there are fundamental requirements needed. These rules are a MUST and not an option that should be incorporated into your lifestyle. During this portion of the chapter we will be discussing:

- **The Blueprint**
- **The Frame**
- **The Foundation**
- **The Roof**

The four elements of a house that is being built from the ground-up are extremely crucial. If one of them is not within city code compliance, the housing inspector is not permitted to issue a permit of occupancy. The home is considered faulty and dangerous.

## I. The Blueprint

The blueprint provides direction for the purpose and usage of the construction. It is a roadmap leading to a particular direction or path.

1. Read Matthew 7:24-26

2. What is this particular scripture saying to you personally?

   _____

   _____

3. What actions can you take to work toward achieving this?

   _____

   _____

## II. The Frame

The frame of the house represents our soul, mind, emotions, intellect, will and imagination. Our soul must be renewed continually by the Word of God. Otherwise, the spirit man will become weaker and weaker. Whoever is ruling you has become the leader.

1. Read James 1:21

2.  What does it mean for you to allow the Word of God to take root in your heart?

    _____

    _____

3.  In what ways have the Word not taken root in your heart?

    _____

    _____

4.  How have you set up self-erected defenses against life's predators?

    _____

    _____

5.  Read Hebrews 4:12

6.  What does it mean that the Word of God divides between soul and spirit?

    _____

    _____

7.  What are some of the effects of the Word of God on a person's life?

    _____

    _____

## III. The Foundation

It is the supportive structure that holds everything in alignment. Without this sure support, everything else that is erected is built on sinking sand.

1.  Read John 6:63.

2.  What does the phrase, "the words that I speak unto you, they are spirit and they are life," mean?

    _____

    _____

3. What areas in your life does *brokenness* need to take place?

   _____

   _____

4. What are some of the deadly emotions that you have allowed to sabotage your life?

   _____

   _____

5. What steps are you "now" willing to take to overcome them?

   _____

   _____

# IV. The Roof

The roof's primary purpose is to shelter from outside elements. Some roofs are designed better than others, and thereby cost more than others to build. There are certain roofs that are FIRE proof, while others are made from cheap material that can't weather a good storm, let alone protect from fire of any degree.

1. What is the necessary ingredient required of prayer?

   _____

   _____

2. Read Psalm 27:14.

3. How does this scripture speak to you?

   _____

   _____

4. What areas in your life have you not "waited" on the Lord?

   _____

   _____

5. What commitment are you willing to undertake to secure a safe "roof"?

   _____

   _____

**Weekly Memory Verse**: *The Word of God is alive and full of power, active, operative, energizing, and effective.* (Hebrews 4:12)

**Weekly Prayer:** Father, I thank You that You are constructing me for greatness. I am a wise woman that is building her house. It's being built with a durable foundation. According to Hebrews 6:1, I am leaving the elementary teaching about Christ and going on to maturity, not laying again the foundation of repentance from dead works and faith toward God. I thank You Father, that I am secure in Your love, certain that I am forgiven, chosen, loved and cared for by You. I thank You that the Scriptures are becoming eternal footprints on my heart by remembering and meditating on Your Word daily.

**Weekly Action List:** What areas of your life will you put into action from Chapter 1 of the book?

## Weekly Character Building Block Word: <u>Attitude</u>

The Oxford Dictionary© defines **attitude** as: posture, position, disposition, aspect, and point of view. Attitude is an inward feeling expressed by behavior. You can see an attitude expressed – long before someone says a word. This characteristic shows on your face, body language, and tone of voice.

Sometimes an attitude can be masked outwardly for a few minutes, but it always makes its way to the surface. Attitudes can hide for only so long before signs of disapproval, disappointment and discontent begin to emerge. We all have that inner conflict warring against spirit and soul.

> *For the good that I wish, I do not do; but I practice the very evil that I do not wish... but I see a different law in the members of my body, waging war against the law of my mind, and making me a prisoner of the law of sin which is in my members. Wretched man that I am! Who will set me free from the body of this death? Thanks be to God through Jesus Christ our Lord! So then, on the one hand I myself with my mind am serving the law of God, but on the other, with my flesh the law of sin.* (Romans 7:19, 23-25)

Since we are all a "Woman Under Construction," let's discuss for a few moments the construction of the attitude.

Everything that is built has a blueprint or plan. Each one of us has been assigned various DNA from our parents. Those genes give voice to who we are, how we respond, how we perceive, calculate and reason. Our personalities usually coincide with our temperaments.

Our environment shapes our perception of how life should appear. Here is where our core "belief system" is formed. Values, judgments, habits, religious convictions are formed at this stage of growth. It's amazing how children are molded based on their surroundings. They may experience poverty, sexual or emotional abuse and other difficult circumstances. Yet, they adapt and go into survival mode!

What I constantly hear every day or have heard that have a lasting impression on my mind inevitably lingers on in my life. Words act as a director of a movie scene or play. Words begin to give direction to the scenes of my life.

Our self-image or how we see ourselves shape the pieces of puzzles in our lives.

*For as he thinks within himself, so he is.* (Proverbs 23:7)

It is impossible to perform consistently in a manner inconsistent with the way we see ourselves. That is the reason it is so important that you gain victories in your life. Despite the size of the victories, you are a winner! The more victories you obtain, the more you believe that "you can" win whatever it is. The more I began to write these chapters, the more I was convinced "yes I can" give you empowering words of wisdom. Each chapter became easier and easier. My confidence was building paragraph by paragraph, page by page. I was actually seeing myself, being a *Woman Under Construction*.

## What is an **attitude**?

It is the collaboration of your past.

It is the mouthpiece of your future.

It is the disappointments of today.

It is transparent in nature.

Its seeds are widespread.

It takes you before great men.

It is a magnet or a repellent.

# CHAPTER 2

# Designed for Purpose

God is the real designer of our lives, and he knows exactly how to construct us. When He created you, He had something great in mind that only you could accomplish. It is through our differences that makes us unique and extraordinary. No need for us to compare ourselves with others. Although there are similarities, there are more differences in each of us that make us irreplaceable! He is the real designer! God knows exactly how to dress us for success!

*And we know that in all things God works for the good of those who love him, who have been called according to His purpose.* (Romans 8:28)

A purpose will cause you to:

**P** URSUE

**U** NMOVED by others

**R** EALIZE your dream

**P** USH through challenges

**O** BSTACLES are conquered, and you

**S** OAR victoriously like an

**E** AGLE

Let's dissect this word: **PURPOSE**.

## Pursue toward the Mark

1. In what ways are you pursuing your purpose in your life?

   _____

   _____

2. What areas do you need to become more aggressive in reaching your goal?

   _____

   _____

## <u>Unmoved</u> by Others

3.  Are there any people in your life that you need to detach from that are draining your energy?

    _____

    _____

4.  Do you need to set boundaries in other relationships? If so, what boundaries need to be established?

    _____

    _____

## <u>Realize</u> Your Dream

5.  What would you do every day as an occupation if money wasn't an issue?

    _____

    _____

6.  What are your strengths?

    _____

    _____

## <u>Push</u> through Challenges

7.  How do you view challenges?

    _____

    _____

8.  In what ways can you work toward conquering those challenges?

    _____

    _____

## <u>Obstacles</u> are Conquered

9.   What stands between you and your dream?

_____

_____

10.  What obstacles have you conquered in your life?

_____

_____

## <u>Soar</u> Victoriously

11.  It's time for you to soar and fly to the next destination on your purpose-driven path. What do
     you see in your view?

_____

_____

12.  Life is a Gentle Teacher. She will keep repeating the lesson until we learn from it. What
     repeated lesson did you learn in order to soar victoriously?

_____

_____

## <u>Eagle</u> Withstands Challenges

13.  An eagle has the ability to soar in turbulent conditions. What circumstances are you facing
     right now that are causing you to be like an eagle?

_____

_____

14.  What are you doing to maintain your focus during this time?

_____

_____

**Weekly Meditation Scripture:** *For whatsoever is born of God overcometh the world: and this is the victory that overcometh the world, even our faith.* (1 John 5:4)

**Weekly Memory Verse:** *And this is the confidence that we have in him, that if we ask anything according to his will, he heareth us. And if we know that he hears us, whatsoever we ask, know that we have the petitions that we desired of him.* (1 John 5:14-15)

**Weekly Prayer:** I thank You Father that the Word of God is forever settled in me, and that my covenant with You is sure and unshakeable. I am an overcomer, and my purpose in life is being fulfilled and established. You are causing me to excel and increase more and more.

**Weekly Action List**: Write out your purpose in life and what matters most to you than anything else. As an added bonus, if you were to have the opportunity to travel anywhere in the world, where would it be?

## Weekly Character Building Block Word: <u>Resourcefulness</u>

A resource is an asset that is available for anticipated needs. The biblical concept of resourcefulness means "to gather." The book of Proverbs 10:5 says, "He that gathered in the summer is a wise son: but he that sleepeth in harvest is a son that causeth shame." The Oxford Dictionary© defines resourcefulness as; ingenious, inventive, imaginative, clever, creative, skillful and smart.

Let's take a few minutes to see how life was preserved through resourcefulness in the Bible. After God determined to judge the world with a flood, He instructed Noah to build an ark in order to preserve his family and all the creatures that could not swim. In addition to preparing space to house the animals, Noah and his family had to be resourceful when gathering enough food to survive during the flood.

An excellent second example of resourcefulness was demonstrated during the preparation for famine throughout the time of Joseph. As a discerning man, Joseph experienced numerous prophetic dreams that were life-changing. In one powerful dream, God instructed Joseph to warn Pharaoh that there would be seven years of abundant harvest followed by seven years of famine. Joseph designed a resourceful plan to prepare for the famine.

> Let them gather all the food of those good years that come,
> and lay up corn under the hand of Pharaoh, and let them
> keep food in the cities. And that food shall be for store to the
> land against the seven years of famine, which shall be in the
> land of Egypt; that the land perish not through the famine,
> (Genesis 41:35-36).

There is a threefold procedure to collect resources.

1.  **Ask and receive**. When we ask God for needed supplies, He has promised to provide them for us. However, in order to receive them, we must take the next two steps.

2.  **Seek and find.** Even though God has already given what we have asked for, we must be diligent to search out that which He has given. This will require insight, initiative and creativity.

3.  **Knock and open.** When we believe we have found what God has given, we must make contact with the people who are involved. "Ask, and it shall be given to you; seek, and ye shall find; knock and it shall be open unto you: For every one that asketh receiveth; and he that seeketh findeth; and to him that knocketh it shall be opened," (Matthew 7:7-8).

The Bible says that God wants to increase you more and more – you and your children. He wants you to grow, swell, enlarge, expand, extend, multiply and flourish. Choose today to become a resourceful woman. Take the brakes off your life and move into drive mode.

# CHAPTER 3

# Break the Fallow Ground

You are doing really well, so keep up the good work. Now, you are well on your way to a victorious life in Christ. In this chapter, we will be dealing with a few issues of the heart, and examining the soil of your heart. The heart is considered to be the core of a person. And, the condition of your heart reflects how you view life. In essence, the heart is the seat of one's hopes, ambitions, affections and desires. In order to break up the fallow ground of your heart, we must examine our true motives and aspirations. Everything hinges on the condition of our heart. Therefore, throughout this exercise we will expose, possibly, some of the hidden layers of self-centeredness, self-justification, self-protective and self-defensive mechanisms. These self-inflicted coping mechanisms have altered our approach to life. Consequently, they have altered our lives. Enough said, let's begin the work.

## Let's Get Real

1.  How does pretense prevent change from the inside out?

    _____

    _____

2.  In what ways are you pretending that things are better than they are?

    _____

    _____

3.  Can you identify a commitment to self-protection in your life? If so, describe it.

    _____

    _____

4.  Who or what do you need to release from your life?

    _____

    _____

5.  What steps are you willing to take?

    _____

    _____

## Test the Quality of the Soil

6.  According to the analogy in Matthew 13:3-8, "*The Parable of the Sower*" what type of soil are you? And why?

    _____

    _____

    ✓ Wayside

    ✓ Rocky

    ✓ Thorny

    ✓ Productive

## Move toward Change

7.  It's time to take stock in your own existence.  What is growing in the ground of your life?

    _____

    _____

8.  What takes up the most space in your life?

    _____

    _____

9.  Jesus made it clear that there were three types of weeds, which one consumes you?

    ✓ The cares, anxieties, worries or interests of this world.

    ✓ The deceitfulness of wealth; the attraction of affluence.

    ✓ The covetousness for things; the magnetism of materialism.

10. Why is it important to "keep" your heart?

    _____

    _____

11. Do you have a divided heart?

    _____

    _____

12. What does it mean to be "broken" before the Lord?

_____

_____

## Read Colossians 3:9-10

13. In what ways have you been wearing a filthy set of ill-fitting clothes?

_____

_____

14. How do you plan to rid yourself of those self-defeating clothes?

_____

_____

**Weekly Memory Verse:** *If any of you lack wisdom, let him ask of God, that giveth to all men liberally, and upbraideth not; and it shall be given him. But let him ask in faith, nothing wavering. For he that wavereth is like a wave of the sea driven with the wind and tossed. For let not that man think that he shall receive anything of the Lord a double-minded man is unstable in all his ways.* (James 1:5-8)

**Weekly Prayer:** Father, I thank You that I have a pure and upright heart. My utmost desire is to please You with my life. I ask You to clear out the layers of self-protectiveness, self-defense, and self-centeredness that have piled over my life. Take out the wayside, the rocky and the thorny ground of my heart. And I no longer have a divided heart, but a heart that is submitted to Your will.

**Weekly Action List**: What areas of your life will you put to action from Chapter 3 of the book?

## Weekly Character Building Block Word: <u>Self-Control</u>

The biblical term for *self-control* is *temperance*. The Greek word for *temperance* is *egkrateia*. It means "inward strength and restraint." Self-control is the virtue of one who masters his desires and passions.

This characteristic is also the inward strength that makes it possible to bring all physical appetites under the control of the Holy Spirit.

Self-control is essential for any believer who wants to excel in the Christian life. The Apostle Paul used the analogy of a runner in a race.
*Know ye not that they which run in a race run all, but one receiveth the prize? So run, that ye may obtain. And every man that striveth for the mastery is temperate in all things.* (1 Corinthians 9:24-25)

Paul then emphasized the eternal value of self-control and the personal sacrifice he was making to achieve it.

> *Now they do it to obtain a corruptible crown; but we are incorruptible. I therefore so run, not as uncertainly; so fight I, not as one that beateth the air: But I keep under my body, and bring it into subjection: lest that by any means, when I have preached to others, I myself should be a castaway.*
> (1 Corinthians 9:25-27)

Self-control comes by instant obedience to the guidance of the Holy Spirit.

> *For what the law could not do, in that it was weak through the flesh, God sending his own Son in the likeness of sinful flesh, and for sin, condemned sin in the flesh: That the righteousness of the law might be fulfilled in us, who walk not after the flesh, but after the Spirit ... Because the carnal mind is enmity against God: for it is not subject to the law of God, neither indeed can be. So then they that are in the flesh cannot please God.* (Romans 8:3-4; 7-8)

Self-control for the Christian means that my "self," my whole person meaning, body, soul, and spirit comes under the control of Christ. This characteristic demonstrates that I am an individual governed by God. My entire life, every aspect of it whether spiritual, moral or physical, has become subject to the sovereignty of God's Spirit. I am a "woman under authority." All of my "body's rights" have been submitted and relinquished over to the Lordship of Jesus Christ.

In order for us to view self-control in the purest form, we can't look at other human beings. Just the word "human," by itself denotes fragility, in capabilities and limitations. The sweetest saints can sometimes turn sour. Instead, we are to look at God himself. We see Him best in Christ. He said that his life was completely under divine control. He came, not to do His own will, but His Father's. The works He carried out were God's own enterprises. Because of this "inner control," He in return was in control of every situation He faced.

Whenever Christ moved, whomever He met, and whatever circumstances He encountered, the remarkable aspect of His life was that He was always in control. Christ was never taken by surprise, nor was He ever caught in a crisis. Jesus was never manipulated, nor was He ever at the mercy of the mob. Even during those desperate, diabolical last hours from the time of His betrayal until His battered body hung on a cruel Roman cross, Christ moved in quiet strength and dignity. And this was because He submitted to God's control.

Sometimes, we wonder why our lives are out of control, unchecked, and chaotic. It is because we have not allowed ourselves to be brought under the sovereignty of the Lordship of Jesus Christ. Unfortunately, many of us simply don't want Him interfering with our lives, attitudes, self-erected rights, and decisions. But, is it really possible to dethrone myself from the throne of my self-made way of responding, reacting, and reasoning?

Yes it is, but there is a price to pay. Inner peace and outer strength come at a high cost. It doesn't just come about by happenstance. Just think, you have been living with yourself for a very long time. It takes reconstructive surgery to change the face of things that have been set in place. To develop self-control means giving up your rights. It goes beyond daydreaming or mental ascent. Self-control digs down to the grassroots, where you relinquish your self-rule and turn yourself over irrevocably to God. One short, self-sacrificing sentence sums up this whole subject.

*O God, not my will, but Thine be done.*

# CHAPTER 4

# Bent Nails

I am so proud of the accomplishment you have made thus far. You are engineered for greatness. This chapter will focus on bouncing back from life's disappointments, devastations and difficulties. In life, every single individual is saved with seemingly unbearable challenges. If not confronted, such dilemmas will spill over into every facet of your life, de-fueling your opportunities and possibilities. Remember, I am your "Woman Under Construction" coach, and I will be mentoring you through each lesson.

Life for me hasn't always been good, so believe me, I can totally relate to your possible circumstances. But, because I pulled myself out of despair, I'm equipped to help pull you out as well. So take my hand. Now, get a tight grip, as I'm beginning to "pull" you out from what once was, to your new state of being.

## Woman Up

1.  What are your assets? What are your liabilities? What people in your inner circle are your assets and liabilities? List your assets and what you can do to maximize them.

   _____

   _____

2.  List your liabilities and what you can do to minimize them.

   _____

   _____

3.  What is your greatest fear in minimizing your liabilities?

   _____

   _____

## Get Up

1.  How do you plan to straighten out the "bent" nails in your life?

   _____

   _____

2.  In what area of your life do you find difficult to forgive yourself? Why?

_____

_____

3.  When you try to get up, what is the enemy always throwing in your face?

_____

_____

## Face Up

1.  Face your most difficult challenge, name it and speak death to it now.

_____

_____

2.  Face your FEARS, what are they?

_____

_____

3.  Face what will happen if you continue to allow your fears to rule your life.

_____

_____

## Give Up

1.  Give up the opportunity to **retaliate**.

2.  Give up your right to be **right**.

3.  Give up your right for **justification**.

**Weekly Meditation Scripture:** *For the word of God is quick, and powerful, and sharper than any two-edged sword, piercing even to the dividing asunder of soul and spirit, and of the joints and marrow, and is a discerner of the thoughts and intents of the heart" (Hebrews 4:12); "Let the word of Christ dwell in you richly in all wisdom; teaching and admonishing one another in psalms and hymns and spiritual songs, singing with grace in your hearts to the Lord" (Colossians 3:16); "This book of the law shall not depart out of thy mouth; but thou shalt meditate therein day and night, that thou mayest observe to do according to all that is written therein: for then thou shalt make thy way prosperous, and then thou shalt have good success" (Joshua 1:8); "Thy word is a lamp unto my feet, and a light unto my path" (Psalm 119:105); and "Howbeit when he, the Spirit of truth, is come,* *he will guide you into all truth: for he shall not speak of himself; but whatsoever he shall hear, that shall he speak: and he will show you things to come* (John 16:13).

**Weekly Prayer:** Father, I thank You for all things have become new in my life; in my relationships, in my family, and in my career. You perfect everything that concerns me, and bring everything into divine alignment and purpose.

**Weekly Memory Verse**: *Therefore, if anyone is in Christ, he is a new creation; old things have passed away; behold all things have become new.* (2 Corinthians 5:17)

**Weekly Action List:** What areas of your life will you put action from Chapter 4 of the book?

## Weekly Character Building Block Word: <u>Patience</u>

Two primary Greek words are translated into the word patience. *Hupomone* is a word that originates from hupo, which means "under," and *meno*, which means to "stay or remain." Patience means to "endure with cheerfulness, and be constant." The root meaning of patience is to; undergo and bear trials; have fortitude and perseverance.

Patience is a reward for properly responding to trials and tribulations. Therefore, the Apostle Paul wrote:

> *We glory in tribulations also: knowing that tribulation worketh patience, and patience, experience hope.* (Romans 5:3-4)

That sounds like a whole lot of work to me. In order to "glory" in tribulations, we must thank God for them and rejoice in the benefits that He designed them to produce. God always desires to produce a glorious harvest in our lives. I often say, "Don't allow your tribulations and trials go to waste. Make them count for something good in your life; allow them to bring a harvest in your life."

> *My brethren, count it all joy when ye fall into divers temptations; knowing this, that the trying of your faith worketh patience. But let patience have her perfect work, that ye may be perfect and entire, wanting nothing.* (James 1:2-4)

The Greek word for perfect is *teleios* which means complete (in various applications of labor, growth, mental and moral character, etc.). To be a qualified leader in ministry you must possess this character.

> *The servant of the Lord must not strive; but be gentle unto all men, apt to teach, patience.* (2 Timothy 2:24)

We also receive the promises of God through our patience.

> *That ye be not slothful, but followers of them who through faith and patience inherit the promises . . . and so after he had patiently endure, he obtained the promise.* (Hebrews 6:12-15)

We also gain God's approval when we wait patiently.
> *For what glory is it, if when ye be buffeted for your faults, ye shall take it patiently? But if, when ye do well, and suffer for it, ye take it patiently, this is acceptable with God.* (1 Peter 2:20)

As previously mentioned, patience will bring a harvest.

*But that on the good ground are they, which in an honest and good heart, having heard the word, keep it, and bring forth fruit with patience.* (Luke 8:15)

And one of my favorite verses is also found within that same scripture.

*In your patience possess ye your souls.* (Luke 8:15).

So that tells me when I possess the quality of patience, I am able to possess my mind, emotions, will, intellect and imagination.

Consider the HGTV remodeling show, *Did You Get the Most Bang for Your Buck?,* where design experts visit three homes to appraise similar renovations performed. Appraisals are based on the type of construction material, overall esthetics and appeal that the home resonates. Some of the homeowners break even, while others have a drastic non-return on their investment. Each contest is concluded with the experts saying, "This house got the best bang for its buck!" I explored this show briefly to simply say, "You get a whole lot of bang for your buck when you practice patience!"

# CHAPTER 5

# Unmasking Walls

Hello again! I'm so Godly proud of all your efforts. It is time for you to experience the Almighty in a new way. I know you must be excited about this wonderful journey of self-awareness, and renovation. This week, we will be taking a journey of "unmasking walls" in our lives. Recently, I spoke to a person who's created a lifestyle of building walls. Not allowing anyone in, but also not giving oneself permission to explore life – beyond self-erected walls. When we develop such walls, it not only keeps people out, but it also keeps us in prison to our own perceptions and judgments. Many have chosen to hide or conceal as a means of protection. And sometimes while doing that, we keep the bad in, fearful of change. It can be extremely difficult for some to trust again, especially when they have been violated, taken advantage of, or just thrown away as a bad bag of garbage. Well, I believe you got the picture I'm trying to paint. Let's do what we are here to do and that's to work out the progress.

## Let the Truth be Told

1. Who or what has hurt you most and kept you from becoming all you can become?

   _____

   _____

2. How has this situation or person crippled your progress in life?

   _____

   _____

3. What is your responsibility in the matter?

   _____

   _____

## The Truth of the Matter

1. How have you tried to bandage your pain?

   _____

   _____

2. Do you see yourself as a victim?

   _____

   _____

3. How many "pity parties" do you have a week?

_____

_____

## The Truth Will Set You Free

1. God's Word says: *Let everything you say be good and helpful.* (Ephesians 4:29). What are you going to begin saying about yourself?

   _____

   _____

2. God's Word says: *God heals the broken-hearted, binding up their wounds.* (Psalms 147:3)

   What wounds do you need healed and mended?

   _____

   _____

3. God's Word says: *Walk by the Spirit, and ye shall not fulfill the lust of the flesh.* (Galatians 5:16) How can you choose today to walk in the spirit?

   _____

   _____

## Know the Truth

1. *For verily I say unto you, that whosoever shall say unto this mountain, be thou removed, and be thou cast into the sea; and shall not doubt in his heart, but shall believe that those things which he saith shall come to pass; he shall have whatsoever he saith.* (Mark 11:22,23)

2. *In righteousness shalt thou be established: thou shalt be far from oppression; for thou shalt not fear: and from terror; for it shall not come near thee.* (Isaiah 54:14)

3. *Why art thou cast down, O my soul? And why art thou disquieted within me? Hope thou in God: for I shall yet praise him, who is the health of my countenance, and my God.* (Psalm 42:11)

**Weekly Memory Verse**: *Looking diligently lest any man fail of the grace of God; lest any roots of bitterness springing up trouble you, and thereby many be defiled.* (Hebrews 12:15)

**Weekly Meditation Scripture:** *And I will bring the blind by a way that they knew not; I will lead them in paths that they have not known: I will make darkness light before them, and crooked things straight. These things will I do unto them and not forsake them.* (Isaiah 42:16)

**Weekly Prayer:** Father, I thank You that I choose to let go of bitterness; to walk in forgiveness, I release myself from resentment, retaliation, anger, hatred, violence and murder. I repent and acknowledge all wrong behaviors. I choose to walk by faith and practice faith and I give the enemy no place in my life.

**Weekly Action List**: List names of people you need a release from that have left bitterness and inability to forgive in your life and pray for them this week.

## Weekly Character Building Block Word: <u>Quality</u>

The Oxford Dictionary© defines the word quality as: characteristic attribute, mark, distinction, and trait. Excellence is considered a type of quality. Although excellence always costs more, it also brings you back dividends. Quality stands out from the crowd, and has a certain distinction.

A woman of quality, substance or excellence makes her presence known, but not by her many words. Rather, she is acknowledged by her few phrases because they are seasoned with grace and wisdom. She is aware of what it means to have a "ministering mouth." In Proverbs 15:7 it reminds us, *The lips of the wise spread knowledge.*

A Godly woman has learned the art of commanding her tongue. When you rule your tongue, then you can have dominion over your life. Many people's lives are out of control because they can't manage their tongue.

Another characteristic of a quality woman is that she exhibits righteous conduct. She clothes herself with dignity. This woman has taken off the "old clothing" of self-rejection, jealousy, envy and self-righteousness. We can learn a lot from the book of Esther in the Bible. Esther was an orphan, and was raised by her cousin, Mordecai. He was a former prisoner of war that was exiled from Jerusalem. Esther had never known how it felt to live as a free woman among her people in her own land. Yet, she was chosen to be queen over the most powerful and influential kingdom of her time. The King of Persia selected Esther to be his queen.

She wasn't afraid to face difficult situations whenever a crisis occurred. With the possible annihilation of the Jews at stake, Esther risked her life to petition the king on their behalf. She waited for God's timing and clear direction. And then, while Esther was fully aware of the possible grave consequences, she acted on her heart and soul's provocation. "I and my maids will fast as you do," she says to Mordecai. "When this is done, I will go to the king, even though it is against the law. And if I perish, I perish." Esther stood out from the other 127 virgins who had submitted their applications for the new queen's job. But it was Esther's quality that caused her to excel in recognition.

# Chapter 6

# Construct Divine Doors

Welcome to Chapter Six. In this chapter, we have explored quite a few serious issues. You may be wondering by now, what have I gotten myself into. Sometimes, you have to tear down to rebuild. Many of you may have hearts of stone because of the abuse and addiction you have suffered. The Holy Spirit is using his Word and love as a chisel to chip away at the stubborn parts of the un-renewed soul. It can be a tedious process, so be patient. Stay encouraged, because when the Word of God is being engrafted into your heart, it is weakening the hard stones of your heart. You may not see an immediate change, but rest assured God is at work. Mistakes can be viewed as temporary inconveniences - not permanent fixtures in your life.

## Let's look at the acronym for Mistakes;

M -     Messages that mirror our decisions in life
I -      Intersections that we must cross to get to another point of destination
S -      Signals that sound an alarm that danger is around
T -      Trials and tests that cause us to examine ourselves
A -      Attitudes and adjustments that must be examined
K -      Keys that we must use to lock old doors and open new doors of opportunity
E -      Exit doors that we must be willing to walk through and never turn around
S -      Strategies and systematic approaches we must incorporate into our lives.

## EXAMINATION

1. When you examine your life, what open doors have you allowed entrance into your life?

2. What have you been exposed to that has opened up certain doors in your life?

3. What void in your life were you trying to fill?

## HIDDEN ADDICTIONS

- What hidden addiction can you relate to;

- Arguing

- Gossip

- Pornography

- Shopping

- Work (workaholism)

- Sex (fantasy, masturbation)

- Lying

- Rage

- Helping needy people

- TV

- Other?

## CATEGORIES OF ADDICTIONS

**Addictions fall into one or more of the following classes;**

- Addictions that stimulate - provide adrenaline and exhilaration

- Addictions that tranquilize - anything that calms us, reduces nervous tension or lowers anxiety

- Addictions that serve some psychological need – striving to achieve power, and self-worth

- Addictions that satisfy unique appetites – food cravings, and alcoholism

## Which if any of these addictions do you fall into?

## Do you locate yourself in any of the following categories?

- A need to escape from worry and anxiety,

- A need to reduce guilty feelings,

- A need for a sense of control and power in one's environment,

- A need to have order and be free of confusion,

- A need to be a "perfect" person

## Have you opened any of the following doors?

- Access Doors of Shame

- The Approval Trap Door

- The Door of Unforgiveness

- The Door of Regret

**Weekly Meditation Scripture**: Colossians 3:8-10, *"But now ye also put off all these; anger, wrath, malice, blasphemy, filthy communication out of your mouth. Lie not one to another, seeing that ye have put off the old man with his deeds; And have put on the new man, which is renewed in knowledge after the image of him that created him."*

**Weekly Memory Verse:** Hebrews 4:12 *"For the word of God is quick, and powerful, and sharper than any two-edged sword, piercing even to the dividing asunder of soul and spirit, and of the joints and marrow, and is a discerner of the thoughts and intents of the heart."*

**Weekly Prayer**: Father I renounce, the sin of addiction, and I close the door of shame, guilt, unforgiveness, the excess need of approval, and the door of regret. And I pray according to I Thessalonians 5:23 that the God of peace sanctify me wholly; and I pray that my spirit, soul and body be preserved blameless unto the coming of our Lord Jesus Christ.

**Weekly Action List**: List the areas in my life that I feel regretful, and shameful. Release yourself, apply the Blood of Jesus, and embrace yourself.

## Weekly Character Building Block Word: <u>Boldness</u>

There is a rich insight in the biblical definitions of boldness. Three Greek words translated *bold* each identify a distinct and important aspect of this quality; (1) Tharrheo – Boldness in the face of death; (2) Parrhesiazomai - Boldness to speak the truth and; (3) Tolmao – Boldness to accomplish great things for God. Webster© defines boldness as; courageous, requiring or showing courage.

When Joshua was commanded to, "be of good courage," he was being told to have boldness – boldness to face death in battle, to speak to his own heart and to the nation, and to do great exploits for God.

Paul had to face beatings, persecutions, and shipwrecks without fear. His secret was the assurance that he was indestructible until his work was done. And, that death would bring him immediately into the eternal presence of the Lord whom he served. Paul had an experience with God that caused him to be able to handle anything and everything that came his way. His knowledge, familiarity and understanding of God caused him to be bold in the face of any obstacle.  He was a fearless and tenacious fighter and did not back away from any opponent.

As we engraft the Scriptures into our lives and meditate on them, we can claim their fulfillment in bold exploits.

Gideon demonstrated boldness when he pulled down his father's false altar and then led three hundred soldiers against the vast hosts of the enemy's army. David also demonstrated boldness as he went out against Goliath. Daniel was bold to speak the truth to King Belshazzar during the drunken feast, in which the king used the sacred vessels from God's Temple.  After hearing God's judgment upon himself and his kingdom, the king honored Daniel.  Honor is given to those who are bold. Anytime an achievement is accomplished by someone, it is most often because they stood out of from the rest or were bold enough to make a difference.

# Chapter 7

# Home Renovation

Whether you are in a spiritual, emotional, financial, or relational renovation, you must keep a check on your "state of mind." Your state of mind denotes your mood or outlook on a particular situation. In order to experience a real renovation it starts with renewing your mind.

*And do not be conformed to this world, but be transformed by the renewing of your mind, that you may prove what is that good and acceptable and perfect will of God. (*Romans 12:2, NKJV).

It's all about transformation. A transformation is to change in character or condition. The exchange of information is critical to success.

Ephesians 4:25 says, *Wherefore putting away lying, speak every man truth with his neighbor; for we are members one of another.* You are affected by those who influence your life. All associations that you have given permission to enter your life impact you. Chaos occurs when you allow others to bring their disorder into your life. You are influenced in three ways; spiritually by God, Angels and demonic spirits. Another influence is through soul impact, which is both good and bad associations. And then you are influenced naturally; by your world and material things.

Well, are you ready now to forge ahead in our journey of renovation and change? Let's get started…

There are several character defects we as women need to transform. Here are a few that we will be exploring in this chapter.

- Anger

- Depression

- Fear

- Pride & Self-Righteousness

- Lying

## Anger

*Be ye angry, and sin not: let not the sun go down upon your wrath* (Ephesians 4:26).

1. Why do you think we are instructed not to let the sun go down and have anger in our hearts?

    _____

    _____

2. Have you ever been angry and all of a sudden, you are on the verge of doing or saying something you know God would not want you to do?

_____

_____

**Solution**: Don't do it. Sit, breathe, and consider the consequences of your actions. If we would only take our time and listen to what the other person is really saying. We might find out that there is no reason to be angry.

3. Have you noticed how a little misunderstanding can turn into a big "mess" if we continue to concentrate on the problem that has us upset?

_____

_____

4. Have you experienced this? And how should you have handled it?

_____

_____

Personally, I have discovered that I can allow a mustard seed of a problem turn into a mountain if I keep on replaying the incident in my head. Does anybody know what I am talking about?

# Depression

There are various forms of depression. It can be chemically-induced because of hormonal imbalance or genetically-inherited, and manifest during preadolescent years. Some, temporarily experience depression due to personal problems. Whatever the cause, the Bible tells us in Matthew 11:28, "Come unto me, all that labor and are heavy laden, and I will give you rest."

1. Have you ever experienced depression? And what were the triggers that brought on the depression?

_____

_____

2. What areas in your life are you not releasing to God?

_____

_____

**Solution:** Put on the garment of praise for the spirit of heaviness, and be thankful to God in all things.

## Fear

Fear is a distressing emotion induced by a perceived threat.

*God did not give us a spirit of fear, but of power and of love and of a sound mind* (2 Timothy 1:7).

1.  Are you fearful about anything?

    _____

    _____

Many people are afraid of change. Ask yourself the following questions:

- What change in your life are you currently resisting?

- Why are you resisting that change?

- What are you afraid of with respect to this change?

- Have you outgrown some things or people in your life?

**Solution:** Receive the love of God. Perfect love cast out fear. Study the Word of God and His unconditional love towards you.

## Pride and Self-Righteousness

Pride is defined as: arrogance, and haughtiness. A prideful person is one that shifts ultimate confidence from God to self. We must always remember that without God we are nothing and can do nothing.

Self-righteousness is when a person is vain and boastful. Our ultimate value doesn't come from our accomplishments, or who we know, but from God. He must become your source in life and He must get the glory from everything good you have done and accomplished in life.

1.  Are you prone to walk in pride? And if so, in what areas?

    _____

    _____

2.  In what area of your life are you taking the credit for, instead of giving God the credit?

    _____

    _____

**Solution:** Begin and practice worshipping God and His supremacy over your life.

## Lying

*Do not lie to each other, since you have taken off your old self with its practices and have put on the new self, which is being renewed in knowledge in the image of its Creator* (Colossians 3:9-10).

1.  Do you find yourself lying, or exaggerating the truth a little?

    _____

    _____

2.  Is it a habit, or are you looking for acceptance?

    _____

    _____

**Solution:** When you find yourself lying and not being completely honest, practice being honest by restating the truth immediately.

**Weekly Meditation Scripture**: *Let not the wise boast of their wisdom or the strong boast of their strength or the rich boast about their riches, but let the one who boasts about this: that they have the understanding to know me, that I am the LORD, who exercises kindness, justice and righteousness on earth, for in these I delight, declares the LORD.* (Jeremiah 9:23-24)

**Weekly Memory Verse**:: *And when you stand praying, if you hold anything against anyone, for them, so that your Father in Heaven may forgive your sin.*(Mark 11:25)

**Weekly Prayer**: Father, I thank You that I exemplify Your nature and character. The Fruits of the Spirit are operating in my life, according to Galatians 5:22, which is love, joy, peace, longsuffering, gentleness, goodness, faith, meekness, temperance against such there is no law.

**Weekly Action List**: Make a list of the Fruits of the Spirit that are lacking in your life. How do you plan to incorporate them into your life?

## Weekly Character Building Block Word: <u>Endurance</u>

It is associated with the physical stamina required for a race. However, the character quality of endurance is much deeper than physical strength. We can say that endurance is experiencing the power of God's love by rejoicing in trials and tribulations.

The Greek word, *Kakopatheo,* means to suffer trouble, be afflicted and undergo hardship. *Anechomai*, another Greek term, means to hold oneself up against, put up with, as well as bear and forbear. Together, both words are translated in the New Testament as the word, *endure*. When you endure, you tenaciously hold on until a good is accomplished. Jacob clung to the angel and declared, "I will not let you go until you bless me!" God not only blessed him but affirmed, *Thy name shall be called no more Jacob, but Israel: for as a prince hast thou power with God and with men, and hast prevailed* (Genesis 32:28).

I have a question and an answer for you. How do we endure? Endurance is based on hope. A runner will endure rigorous and painful training for the hope that he will win the race. Jesus endured the cross and despised the shame of this type of death. For His release came in the joy of knowing that His death would conquer Satan and bring redemption to the redeemed for all eternity.

When trials and temptations come, we are to meet and endure them with the four following responses:

1. **Thank God for each trial.** Now for the record, when I say trial, I'm not speaking about sickness or lack. The Bible says, they *work together for good to them that love God.* (Romans 8:28) Job endured a great affliction of trial because he understood this point *the LORD gave, and the LORD hath taken away; blessed be the name of the LORD* (Job 1:21). Sometimes, God will place people in your life to take you to a certain destination, but will bring someone else in your life to take you to your next destination. And then, another person may come along to take you to your final purpose. Some mentors in life are temporary, while others are life mentors.

2. **Rejoice in all things.** I can rejoice because I know the final outcome, which is the point that "I Win!" Over every trial, I am a conqueror. The final transcripts have been written, and all I must do is place my name in the scripture. *Because I have set Him on high under the wings of the Almighty* (see Psalm 91).

3. **Cry out when necessary.** Some situations should not be endured, and God will bring relief when we cry out to Him. *Call upon me in the day of trouble: I will deliver thee, and thou shalt glorify me* (Psalm 50:15).

4. **Overcome by doing good.** *Be not overcome of evil, but overcome evil with good.* (Romans 12:21) So, I must make a divine exchange here. I can't conquer anything by submitting to the evil in someone else. That is what I'm doing when I choose to repay evil for evil.

Now, let's examine a few biblical examples of endurance:

- Elijah stood against the evil of his day and was hunted down, but he was faithful to the end (1 Kings 19).

- John the Baptist was imprisoned for his stand on divorce and remarriage, yet he remained faithful to his death (Matthew 11:11).

- Daniel maintained Godly standards during the reign of four kings. He was tested when others attempted to take his life, but he endured to the end (Daniel 1:21).

- Luke endured with Paul to the end (2 Timothy 4:11).

- Damas failed the endurance test. Rather than serve Paul in prison, he left to enjoy the pleasures of this world (2 Timothy 4:10).

# CHAPTER 8

# Create a Stunning Home

God is beautifying your life. He is making everything brand new and exquisite in His sight. You are what you know; you manifest what you know; you prosper by what you know; and you perish by what you don't know.

> *This book of the law shall not depart out of thy mouth; but thou shalt mediate therein day and night, that thou mayest observe to do according to all that is written therein; for then thou shalt make thy way prosperous, and then thou shalt have good success.*(Joshua 1:8)

God wants us to succeed in all our endeavors and bear fruit in all we do. You are a life-giver by nature. The Almighty gave the female a powerful responsibility in the world: to give birth. How amazing is that? You beautify life; create something out of nothing, process ideas and words. You have the capacity to multiply what you have been given. You are the solution to somebody, and with your flare, you add spice to life. What would the world be without you?

## Reasons You Have Value

- According to Genesis 1:26:    You are created in the image of God.
- According to Romans 6:6:    Your old man is crucified.
- According to Ephesians 1:4:    You are chosen.
- According to Philippians 1:6:    Jesus is working in you.
- According to Ephesians 2:10:    You are His work of art.
- According to Galatians 5:1:    Christ has made you free.

## Celebrate Yourself

1. In what ways do you need to begin to celebrate yourself?

   _____

   _____


2. What is unique about you?

   _____

   _____

3. What do you add to society?

_____

_____

## Beautification

1. In what ways do you need to begin to beautify yourself on the outside?

_____

_____

2. What are your favorite colors? And why?

_____

_____

3. What can you do to bring "you" into your home?

_____

_____

## Inward Beautification

➢ Do you make time to soak in the presence of God?

➢ What roots do you need to cut out of your life?

➢ How are these roots sabotaging your growth and causing you to bear unhealthy fruit in your life?

➢ What task is God preparing you for?

➢ What steps are you taking to move toward your destiny?

➢ Your inward beauty should tell a story. What life lessons have you learned?

➢ You want to live life rather than letting life live you. In what ways can you begin to live life fully?

**Weekly Meditation Scripture:** The book of Isaiah 40:31 reads, *But they that wait upon the LORD shall renew their strength; they shall mount up with wings as eagles; they shall run, and not be weary; and they shall walk, and not faint.*

**Weekly Memory Verse**: *Death and life are in the power of the tongue; and they that love it shall eat the fruit thereof.* (Proverbs 18:21)

**Weekly Prayer**: Father, I thank You for beautifying me on the inside and adorning me with Your unconditional love to all mankind. Show me how to be kind, patient, and gentle. Purify me and wash me clean through Your Word, that I may represent me and be an example of Your unfailing love.

**Weekly Action List**: Make a list of all your beautiful qualities, and attributes, and then rejoice over them.

## Weekly Character Building Block Word: <u>Meekness</u>

In studying the word "meek", I learned the Hebrew word is *anavah*. It comes from a word that means "to abase oneself, to chasten and humble oneself." The Webster Dictionary© defines it as; showing patience and humility; gentle.

Meekness is vital because it is the one quality that Jesus used to describe Himself:

*Learn of me; for I am meek and lowly in heart* (Matthew 11:29)

Thus, the more we understand and develop meekness, the more we take on the nature of the Lord Jesus Christ.

I've always associated meekness with being weak and somewhat fragile. I thought it meant when a person was unable to hold his own, so to speak. However, I learned it is a quality that every believer should have if she is aspiring to become more like Him.

*The spirit of the Lord God is upon me; because the Lord hath anointed me to preach good tidings unto the meek.* ( Isaiah 61:1)

Jesus associated Himself with preaching the good news to those who were humble. Not everyone has the capacity to hear the truth, receive it, act on it, and incorporate it in his life. Jesus was saying, "I have been sent to those who are willing to chasten themselves." In other words, they need to possess the wherewithal to correct, discipline and reprimand themselves. And, in order to do that, you have to receive the Word with meekness.

Interestingly, many people feel as if they don't need a Savior. They have become what I call a, "self-made God" in their own eyes. However, Jesus is informing us that the Gospel can only be received by those who know that they can't do this thing called "life" alone. It is by the quality of meekness that one is able to make God's Word a vital part of his mind, will, emotions, and can thereby conquer the destructive habits of life.

*Wherefore lay apart all filthiness and superfluity of naughtiness, and receive with meekness the engrafted word, which is able to save your souls.* (James 1:21, NKJV)

# CHAPTER 9

# Your House Needs First-Rate Piping

Mental anguish is extreme anxiety or emotional torment. It is an emotion triggered by thoughts of past or present experiences. Emotional torment can be self-inflicted, provoked by non-productive choices or destructive soul-ties, as well as a dependency on an unhealthy person. This negative feeling can also be a result from being manipulated or pushed around consistently. Another means of creating emotional torment draws from experiencing aggressive behavior, which can include violence.

*My people are destroyed for lack of knowledge; because thou hast rejected knowledge, I will also reject thee, that thou shalt be no priest to me; seeing thou hast forgotten the law of thy God, I will also forget thy children.*(Hosea 4:6)

- What you know affects how you believe; wicked or righteous

- What you know affects the quality of life you live; impoverished or prosperous

- What you know affects your future; an improved life

- What you know affects your eternal destination; salvation

- What you know determines your performance in life; serving your community

You and I have been taught and trained all our lives to respond in certain ways to particular circumstances. Our hidden training comes out under pressure. Therefore, when a difficult situation occurs, your training takes over.

This week we will be dealing with "real issues." Are you ready for the journey?

## Real Issues

1. Have you been victimized by a sexual predator?

   _____

   _____

2. Abused women carry tons of unwarranted guilt. What guilt are you still carrying?

   _____

   _____

3. I have heard numerous stories where young girls, now adults, were not protected by their mothers or relatives. Sadly, they were taken advantage of time and again. Were you not protected by a family member?

_____

_____

## Trust Issues

1. Do you find it difficult to trust members of the opposite sex, including your significant other, because of the violation?

_____

_____

2. Have you begun your healing process of forgiveness?

_____

_____

3. As a result of the violation, do you have issues with trusting God?

_____

_____

## Hot Issues

1. What are your most challenging mental thoughts?

_____

_____

2. How can you keep the thoughts from germinating?

_____

_____

4. How and when did these thoughts originate?

_____

_____

**Weekly Meditation Scripture:** *You will keep him in perfect peace, whose mind is stayed on you because he trusts in you* (Isaiah 26:3).

**Weekly Memory Scripture:** *Be anxious for nothing, but in everything by prayer and supplication, with thanksgiving, let your requests be made known to God; and the peace of God, which surpasses all things will guard your hearts and minds through Christ Jesus. Finally, Brethren, whatever things are true, whatever things are noble, whatever things are just, whatever things are pure, whatever things are of good report, if there is any virtue and if there is anything praiseworthy – meditate on these things.* (Philippians 4:6-8, NLT).

**Weekly Prayer:** Father, I declare I no longer experience mental anguish. Today is the day I stop accepting my temporary situation as my future, permanent situation. Despite my current circumstances, I make up my mind to get on with my life, in Jesus' name.

**Weekly Action List:** How and what methods are you planning on enforcing in your life to win over the battlefield within your mind?

## Weekly Character Building Block Word: <u>Truthfulness</u>

One Hebrew word for truth is *emeth*. It means: stability, certainty, right and sure. Truthfulness originates from the word, aman, which is: to build up or support; foster as a parent or nurse; be firm or faithful; permanent, steadfast and verified. Truth is the foundation upon which any building rests. Only what is birthed in truth can prevail – deception leads to destruction.

*Sanctify them through thy truth: thy word is truth* (John 17:17)

God's Word is truth. His Word is also the final authority of all things. The truth of God's Word is firm and steadfast. It is reliable, and without deliberation. So exactly what does the truth do? First of all, there is power in truth because it is the very essence of God. The truth brings us into Christ and the light, as well as purifies our souls. The power of truth has the ability to free us.

*And ye shall know the truth, and the truth shall make you free.* (John 8:32)

Truth frees us by tearing down false ideas and conclusions that keep us in fear and bondage.

Truth cleanses us from iniquity by "mercy and truth iniquity is purged: and by the fear of the LORD men depart from evil" (Proverbs 16:6). The first step of purging is crying out to God for mercy. Secondly, you must confess and repent.

*If we confess our sins, he is faithful and just to forgive us our sins, and to cleanse us from all unrighteousness* (1 John 1:9)

The third step is to fill our hearts with God's truth and meditate on it day and night.

*Wherewithal shall a young man cleanse his way? By taking
heed thereto according to thy word. With my whole heart
have I sought thee: O let me not wander from thy
commandments. Thy word have I hid in mine heart, that
I might not sin against thee* (Psalm 119:9-11)

# Chapter 10

# The Heart of the Home

Whatever state you are in, whether single, divorced or married, it is important how you build the core of your present state.

*The wise woman builds her house but with her own hands the foolish one tears her down.* (Psalm 14:1)

A wise woman builds her house with the following: an intimate relationship with God, a heart to please God, a life of prayer, and a life of service in helping others. All these ingredients are crucial in building a solid foundation of a wise woman. While there are many women in the world, a lot less of them are wise in their dealings. To be a wise woman one must control her thoughts as well as her tongue.

*Behold, he travaileth with iniquity, and hath conceived mischief, and brought forth falsehood. He made a pit and digged it, and is fallen into the ditch which he made. His mischief shall return upon his own head, and his violent dealing shall come upon his own fate.* (Psalm 7:14-16, KJV)

Through our thoughts and our words, we often dig holes for ourselves. A hole is where there is no forward progression, no forward motion. You are trapped and sometimes buried in the hole you dug for yourself. So how do you get out of the hole? Stop digging – the more you dig, the deeper the hole, and the harder it is to get out. And then you must look up. Looking down has no value and has not helped your situation. Finally, you need to ask for help from someone who is not in the hole with you. Since I'm your "Woman Under Construction" coach, therefore, I will assist you in coming out of the hole. Let's proceed with "The Heart of the Home" journey.

## Test of Character

1. What type of man, in your estimation, is marriage material?

   _____

   _____

2. How do you judge his character?

   _____

   _____

3. What mistakes have you made in the past in judging a man's character?

   _____

   _____

## Mr. Right

1. What does he add to your life?

   _____

   _____

2. Is he an asset or liability? Why?

   _____

   _____

3. Does he make you a better person?

   _____

   _____

## Contentment

1. Why is it important to be content with yourself, before entering a relationship?

   _____

   _____

2. Why do you want a man?

   _____

   _____

3. Are you content with yourself?

   _____

   _____

## Reflect

1. What were the things that attracted you to your husband or ex-husband?

   _____

   _____

2.  Were you in denial or temporary insanity?

_____

_____

3.  If you were to do it over again, in choosing Mr. Right, would you choose him to enter into a relationship?

_____

_____

## What is Your Resume?

1.  What attributes do you have to offer a husband?

_____

_____

2.  What areas do you need healing before entering another relationship?

_____

_____

3.  Are you an asset or liability? And if so, why?

_____

_____

## A Good Thing

1.  The Bible says, "When a man finds a woman he finds a good thing he obtaineth favor from the Lord." Do you bring value to your husband? And if so, how?

_____

_____

2.  How are you to build him up?

_____

_____

3.   Does he trust you totally?

_____

_____

**Weekly Meditation Scripture**: *The wise woman builds her house, but with her own hands the foolish one tears her down.* (Proverbs 14:1)

**Weekly Memory Verse**: *Not that I speak in respect of want; for I have learned, in whatsoever state I am, therewith to be content.* (Philippians 4:11)

**Weekly Prayer**: Father, I thank You that I am a virtuous woman, the heart of my husband trusts me, and I cause him to have favor with You and men. Thank You Father, for giving me the desires of my heart, and preparing me for the man You have for me. Thank You Father, for healing me from past, unhealthy relationships, and thank You for teaching me how to be content in my state.

**Weekly Action List**: What ways can you becomes a better person for your mate?

## Weekly Character Building Block Word: <u>Contentment</u>

In Hebrew, the word, "ya'al," is : to show willingness; to undertake; to agree to or accept. Contentment is used to describe a person resolved to do something or allow a situation to remain the same. In a biblical sense, contentment is realizing that God has already provided everything I need for my present and future happiness.

Contentment occurs as we realize that God is all we really need, and understanding that He will never leave us. We can be satisfied in Him, knowing that He is the Supplier of all our physical and spiritual needs.

*Be content with such things as ye have: for he hath said, I will never leave thee, nor forsake thee.* (Hebrews 13:5)

Contentment is contrary to human nature and must be learned. With all that our society demands, we are constantly striving for the next new house, a car upgrade with all the comforts of life, as well as the latest computer featuring the newest gadgets. Many, highly anticipate the newest cell phone fully loaded with the latest applications.

Yet, Adam and Eve had the perfect environment, and they were not content. They had prime health, a healthy marriage, a beautiful garden and daily fellowship with God, Himself. Nevertheless, the couple believed the lie that God had not provided everything they needed for their present and future happiness. If Adam and Eve were not content in the Garden of Eden, what hope is there for the rest of us, apart from the spiritual insight that comes from God? May we, with Paul, be able to say, "Not that I speak in respect of want: for I have learned, in whatsoever state I am in, therewith to be content," (Philippians 4:11).

Now, let's get the record straight here. The aforementioned verse didn't mean that you are to settle for whatever life throws your way. But, you are to continually strive for the "better" that life has to offer you. And, simultaneously, continually believe God for the BEST. You have to determine your

Best Life! You can't base it on what others possess, where they live or what they drive. Now, the question you may be asking is, "How do I obtain more contentment?"

Contentment is achieved by exchanging worldly possessions for more of Christ. Paul said:

*Yea, doubtless, and I count all things but loss for the Excellency of the knowledge of Christ Jesus my Lord: for whom I have suffered the loss of all things, and do count them but dung, that I may win Christ.* (Philippians 3:8)

In one sense, life is a continual exchange. We exchange time on the job for money. Money is then traded for food, and food is bartered for strength. A wise person will exchange things of lesser value for things of greater value. Jesus warned about the conflict between temporal things and eternal riches when He spoke of the seed falling into different types of soil.

*He also that received seed among the thorns is he that heareth the word; and the care of this world, and the deceitfulness of riches, choke the word, and he becometh unfruitful.* (Matthew 13:22)

But if God finds you to be trustworthy in small things at first, He will quickly entrust you with greater riches. Few are the men and women to whom God can give great wealth. It often goes to their heads. They don't know how to handle it. Instead of being at church and carrying out their obligations, they are found in some distant vacation hideaway or tanning on the white sands near crystal blue seas. Perhaps, the missing church member is putting on lush, green grass with his well-stocked golf bag.

When you are able to clothe the naked, feed the hungry, heal the sick, educate the illiterate, bring good news to the lost and assist the hurts of the of a sick and suffering world, then you have discovered the true meaning of living outside your personal wants and desires.

I can then say, "You can be trusted with the riches of the world because you have learned the art of contentment."

# Chapter 11

# Build for Your Future

Every now and then, building for your future involves disconnecting in order to connect to a better source. Releasing old associations and creating new healthy relationships sometimes consists of stopping destructive habits. At any rate, you are up for the challenge. You wouldn't have made it to Chapter 11 if you weren't ready for the new challenge. However, releasing the old, and embracing the new, brings a lot of emotion we would rather avoid. Have no fear. There are new opportunities awaiting you. So, welcome the new open doors awaiting you. Through the process of "Woman Under Construction," you have removed some layers of the affects of broken dreams, failures, and shattered homes. You are stronger than you think, so remember the past is dead. It's time for you to bury it! And move on…

## Open Doors

1.  What opportunities are you anticipating for this next phase of your life?

    _____

    _____


2.  What is your passion in life?

    _____

    _____


3.  What puts a smile on your face, every time you think about it?

    _____

    _____


## Dead Weight

1.  What dead weight do you have to get rid of to build for your future? For example; life

    suckers, manipulators, critics, pretenders, etc.

    _____

    _____

2. How do you plan to disregard the dead weight? Are you up for the challenge?

_____

_____

3. Sometimes dead weight is memories. What memories of the past are weighing you down?

_____

_____

## It's Time to Bounce Back

1. What business opportunities, promotion, and increase do you see in your near future?

_____

_____

2. What books are you preparing to read? Are there any seminars you plan on attending to enhance your future?

_____

_____

3. It's time to recover all, what is first on your list of recovery?

_____

_____

**Weekly Meditation Scripture**: *Do not call to mind the former things, or ponder things of the past. Behold, I will do something new, now it will spring forth; will you not be aware of it? I will even make a roadway in the wilderness, rivers in the desert.* (Isaiah 43:18-19)

**Weekly Memory Verse**: *And, behold, there was a woman who had a spirit of infirmity eighteen years, and was bowed together, and could in no wise lift up herself. And when Jesus saw her, he called her to him, and said unto her, woman, thou art loosed from thine infirmity. And he laid his hands on her; and immediately she was made straight, and glorified God.* (Luke 13:11-13)

**Weekly Prayer**: Father, I thank You that my life is being transformed. I'm a new creature in Christ Jesus. You are glorifying my life, putting it on display to show what You will do with a life that is submitted, yielded and obedient to Your Word.

**Weekly Action Item**: Write out your plans and goals and how you plan to implement each item.

## Weekly Character Building Block Word: <u>Determination</u>

One Hebrew translation of the word, "determined," is *amar*: to say in one's heart; to think; to command; to promise; to intend. Webster's II New Riverside Dictionary© defines determination as; to decide or settle authoritatively or conclusively; to reach a decision, as after consideration or calculation.

Determination deals with a mindset prior to a task, while endurance involves the carrying out of the task. To be determined means possessing the ingredient required to complete a task, assignment or purpose.

Let's look at a few folks who demonstrated this characteristic in the Bible. First, there was Solomon who was "determined to build a house for the name of the LORD, and a house for his kingdom," (2 Chronicles 2:11). Now, consider Daniel, who "purposed in his heart that he would not defile himself with the portion of the king's meat, nor with the wine which he drank: therefore he requested of the prince of the eunuchs that he might not defile himself," (Daniel 1:8). And third, the Apostle Paul, "determined not to know anything among you, save Jesus Christ, and him crucified," (1 Corinthians 2:2).

Upon reviewing the Scriptures, I found that all of the characters had a heart conviction. It takes more than a rational, head conviction to have determination. I can "wish" something forever, but if my heart and conviction of that desire is not present, I will not have the determination to follow through with my plans. We have heard time and again that life is choice-driven. The choices that we make will ultimately determine our outcome.

So, if we make the right choices, it will be well with us. Making choices equals losses or gains, pain or pleasure. Moses chose to suffer with the children of Israel. He recognized that *The reproach of Christ (brought) greater riches than the treasures in Egypt: for he had respect unto the recompense of the reward.* (Hebrews 11:26).

I have counseled women who experienced the grave mistake of making wrong decisions in life, which unfortunately left them in difficult, unwanted circumstances. There are some options in life that can't be altered. We just have to learn to live with the hand that we are dealt as a result of our choices. So, how do you develop determination?

First, you must have a conviction or a cause. Second, you have to know your purpose for the determination. And third, you should be able to display patience to endure until you see the manifested result.

# Chapter 12

# Before & After Pictures

Before and after pictures reveal the, "change," in a person's appearance, attitude, and spiritual prowess. As they say, "a picture tells a thousand words." Change sometimes can be a bit frightening, because it always involves the unknown. Oftentimes, we find ourselves, wanting change, yet fearing its effects. Whenever you decide to change and move your life to the next level of accomplishment, you must fasten your mental and spiritual seatbelts. It may be a while before you reach a comfortable level again. Eventually, you will reach it, but you must endure the turbulence of change in order to grow. So, why change? Here are four reasons why you cannot succumb to your fear of change:

1. You have not yet tapped into your full potential.

2. Your children, relatives and friends are counting on you.

3. You want to live life to the fullest, and experience a life without excuses.

4. You want to be happy.

## Change

1. Have you outgrown some things or people in your life?

   _____

   _____

2. In order to become more in demand in your career, what do you need to change?

   _____

   _____

3. What fear do you need to let go in order to change?

   _____

   _____

## Moving Up

1. Everything in life costs something. What dream thieves are you going to give up in order move up? For example, time, people, situations, money, etc.

   _____

   _____

2. What mentors do you have in your life to assist with your dream?

   _____

   _____

3. We all need encouragers on our journey through life. List seven people you believe can help you on your journey to greatness.

   _____

   _____

## Recognize Your Gifts

1. Know your gifts, talents and abilities. Share them with someone. Write them down. This is no time for modesty, besides no one is watching.

   _____

   _____

2. What do you expect out of your life?

   _____

   _____

3. List the names of people who know your gifts, talents and abilities.

   _____

   _____

4.  Look for an accountability partner that knows your gifts and check-in with them once a week

regarding your progress.

_____

_____

**Weekly Meditation Scripture**: _Trust (lean on, rely on, and be confident) in the Lord, and do good, so shall you dwell in the land of feed surely on His faithfulness and truly you shall be fed._ (Psalm 37:3).

**Weekly Memory Verse**: _Therefore, my beloved brethren, be ye steadfast, unmovable, always abounding in the work of the Lord, forasmuch as ye know that your labour is not in vain in the Lord._ (1 Corithians 15:58)

**Weekly Prayer**:  Father, I thank You that I have been rescued out of the kingdom of darkness and was transferred into the kingdom of God's dear son, according to Colossians 1:13. My spirit has been recreated, and instantly everything about me changed. Your purpose, Your destiny, Your reason for me living, and Your plan for my life is becoming clearer and clearer each day.

**Weekly Action List**:  Make a list of the most powerful, personal chapters in the book, **Woman Under Construction** that have ministered to you. Make a commitment to sow into someone else's life this week by sharing what you have learned.

## Weekly Character Building Block Word: <u>Now</u>

The Oxford Dictionary© defines the word, "now" as: at present, right now, at the present time or moment, under or in the present circumstances or conditions in the present climate.

It's time to move, expand, dream again and live. There is a major difference between "living" and "living a quality life." Mere existence is accepting the status quo – living the ordinary life. But, it's "Now time" to move into your full potential. Eleanor Roosevelt once said, "You must do the thing you cannot do." That's a powerful and thought-provoking statement. Mrs. Roosevelt simply was saying, "You must take a few risks in life just to prove to yourself, 'I can do this."

First, you should stop thinking in generalities, and focus your attention on one specific task to do now. With respect to our tool book lesson, it's time to exercise your gifts! No more procrastination! Nor should you continue analyzing the reasons for your procrastination. Second, don't let yourself get away with cop-outs! Get tough with yourself. Because the human mind, much like the human body, has an incredible ability to adjust to the demands made on it. And, when the demands are steady, regular and consistent, the result is growth, power and a greater ease of performance. Make a decision. At least you're moving in some direction. Finally, manage your time! You can never retrieve time. There is always an opportunity to retrieve lost wages, but time never stands still, nor does it wait for you to catch up.

*For I know the plans I have for you, declares the Lord, plans to prosper you and not to harm you, plans to give you hope and a future.* (Jeremiah 29:11)

This verse ought to give us a great deal of hope and comfort, as well as a sense of anticipation. If you have breath, you have purpose. And it is NOW time to do it.

## About The Author

Linda G. Hodge is a wife, mother, grandmother, pastor, motivational speaker, and now she adds the title of author.  For more than a decade, Linda has produced conferences, seminars, and extreme makeovers designed to uplift, support and empower women with the tools to renovate and restore their God-given purpose in life.  Her commitment to abused women and children is unwavering.   By popular demand, and encouragement, Linda was inspired to write her self-help manual, *Woman Under Construction*  to help bring more women to a place of healing and success.

Linda G. Hodge co-pastors Living Praise Christian Center with her husband, Dr. Fred L. Hodge, Jr. in Chatsworth and Lancaster, California. They have five children and seven grandchildren.